abc

illustrated by MARGARET CHAMBERLAIN

Aa

Acknowledgments
The editor and publishers would like
to thank Mary Haselden for her help in selecting rhymes
for this book and Elaine Saffer, who wrote *I like ice cream;
The xylophone song* and *I'm going to the zoo.*

Ladybird books are widely available, but in case of
difficulty may be ordered by post or telephone from:

Ladybird Books – Cash Sales Department
Littlegate Road Paignton Devon TQ3 3BE
Telephone 0803 554761

A catalogue record for this book is available
from the British Library

Published by Ladybird Books Ltd Loughborough Leicestershire UK
Ladybird Books Inc Auburn Maine 04210 USA

Five rosy apples by the cottage door,
One tumbled off the twig,
and then there were four.

Four rosy apples hanging on the tree,
The farmer's wife took one,
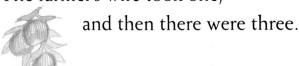and then there were three.

Three rosy apples, what shall I do?
I think I'll have one,
and then there'll be two.

Two rosy apples hanging in the sun,
You have the big one,
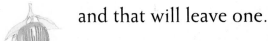and that will leave one.

One rosy apple, soon it is gone,
The wind blew it off the branch,
and now there are none.

The wheels on the bus
Go round and round,
Round and round,
Round and round.
The wheels on the bus
Go round and round,
All day long.

The horn on the bus
Goes peep, peep, peep ...*etc.*

The windscreen wiper on the bus
Goes swish, swish, swish ...*etc.*

The people on the bus
Bounce up and down ...*etc.*

I had a little cherry stone
And put it in the ground,
And when next year I went to look,
A tiny shoot I found.

The shoot grew upwards day by day,
And soon became a tree.
I picked the rosy cherries then,
And ate them for my tea.

Miss Polly had a dolly
Who was sick, sick, sick.
So she 'phoned for the doctor
To be quick, quick, quick.

The doctor came
With his bag and his hat,
And he rapped at the door
With a rat-tat-tat.

He looked at the dolly
And he shook his head.
Then he said, "Miss Polly,
Put her straight to bed."

He wrote on a paper
For a pill, pill, pill;
"I'll be back in the morning
With my bill, bill, bill."

 Ee

An elephant walks like this and that,
He's terribly tall and terribly fat.
He has no fingers,
He has no toes,
But goodness gracious, what a nose!

The farmer's in his den,
The farmer's in his den,
Eee-aye-eee-aye,
The farmer's in his den.

The farmer wants a wife
...etc.
The wife wants a child
...etc.
The child wants a nurse
...etc.
The nurse wants a dog
...etc.
The dog wants a bone
...etc.
We all clap the bone
...etc.

Here are Grandma's spectacles,
And here is Grandma's hat,
And here's the way
She folds her hands,
And puts them in her lap.

Here are Grandpa's spectacles,
And here is Grandpa's hat,
And here's the way
He folds his arms,
And takes a little nap.

Raise your hands above your head,
Clap them one, two, three;
Rest them now upon your hips,
Slowly bend your knees.

Up again and stand up tall,
Put your right foot out;
Shake your fingers, nod your head,
And twist yourself about.

I like ice cream,
It's my favourite treat.
I like ice cream,
That's what I like to eat.
And I like ice cream any time I can.
Oh, I like ice cream,
Here's the ice cream man.

Jj

Jack-in-the-box...
Jumps up like this!
He makes me laugh
As he waggles his head.
I gently press him down again
Saying, "Jack-in-the-box,
You must go to bed."

Old King Cole
Was a merry old soul,
And a merry old soul was he;
He called for his pipe,
And he called for his bowl,
And he called for his fiddlers three.

Ladybird, ladybird,
Fly away home,
Your house is on fire
And your children all gone;
All except one
And that's little Ann
And she's crept under
The frying pan.

There's such a tiny little mouse,
Living safely in my house.
Out at night he'll softly creep,
When everyone is fast asleep;
But always in the light of day
He'll softly, softly creep away.

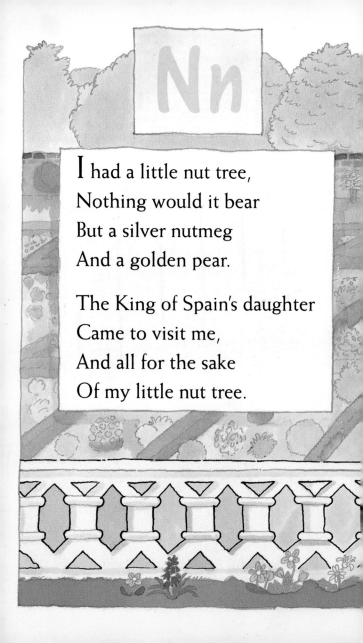

Nn

I had a little nut tree,
Nothing would it bear
But a silver nutmeg
And a golden pear.

The King of Spain's daughter
Came to visit me,
And all for the sake
Of my little nut tree.

Oo

"Oranges and lemons,"
Say the bells of St Clements.

"You owe me five farthings,"
Say the bells of St Martins.

"When will you pay me?"
Say the bells of Old Bailey.

"When I grow rich,"
Say the bells at Shoreditch.

"When will that be?"
Say the bells of Stepney.

"I'm sure I don't know,"
Says the great bell at Bow.

Here comes the candle
    to light you to bed,
Here comes the chopper
    to chop off your head.
Chip, chop, chip, chop
    the last man's... head.

Pp

Five little peas
in a peapod pressed;
One grew, two grew
and so did all the rest.
They grew and grew
and did not stop,
Until one day the peapod popped.

Qq

The Queen of Hearts
She made some tarts,
All on a summer's day.
The Knave of Hearts
He stole those tarts,
And took them clean away.

The King of Hearts
Called for the tarts,
And beat the knave full sore.
The Knave of Hearts
Brought back the tarts,
And vowed he'd steal no more.

Rr

Ring a ring o' roses,
A pocket full of posies,
A-tishoo, a-tishoo,
We all fall down.

The king has sent his daughter
To fetch a pail of water,
A-tishoo, a-tishoo,
We all fall down.

The robin on the steeple
Is singing to the people,
A-tishoo, a-tishoo,
We all fall down.

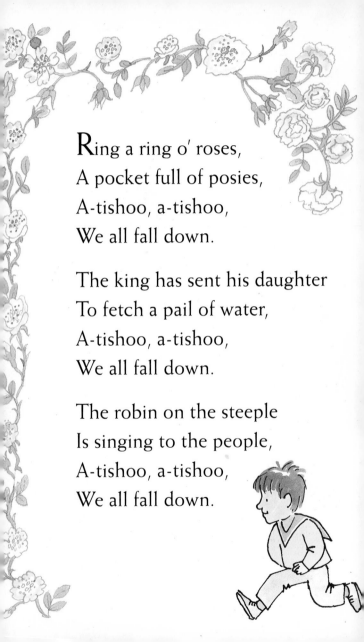

I saw a slippery, slithery snake
Slide through the grasses,
Making them shake.

He looked at me with his beady eye.
"Go away from my
Pretty green garden," said I.

"SSS," said the slippery,
                    slithery snake,
As he slid through the grasses,
Making them shake.

The tortoise can't go out to play
Or sell his house or rent it;
For when he moves,
His house moves too
And nothing can prevent it.

Uu

Please open your umbrella,
Please open your umbrella,
Please open your umbrella,
And shield me from the rain.

The shower is nearly over,
The shower is nearly over,
The shower is nearly over,
So shut it up again.

Vv

Roses are red,
Violets are blue,
Sugar is sweet,
And so are you!

There's a worm
At the bottom of the garden,
And his name is Wiggly Woo.
There's a worm
At the bottom of the garden,
And all that he can do,
Is to wiggle all night,
And wiggle all day.
Whatever else the folk may say,
There's a worm
At the bottom of the garden,
And his name is Wiggly,
Wig, Wig, Wiggly,
Wig, Wig, Wiggly Woo, oo, oo.

Last year for my birthday
I got a xylophone.
Although I couldn't play it,
I learnt how on my own.
Now I know some music
And I love the bouncy tone.
So I play for hours each day
Upon my xylophone.

Yankee Doodle came to town,
Riding on a pony;
He stuck a feather in his cap
And called it Macaroni.

I'm going to the zoo,
Going to the zoo.
I'll see lions and tigers,
And a jumping kangaroo.
I'm going to the zoo.
There'll be a gnu,
And lots of things to see and do.

When I go to the zoo,
I'll watch the monkeys swinging by,
And tall giraffes
With their heads in the sky.
The sea lions playing in their pool,
And polar bears
Looking snowy white and cool.